MAKING THE GRADE • at Ch

EASY POPULAR CHRISTMAS PIECES FOR YOUNG FLAUTISTS.
SELECTED AND ARRANGED BY JERRY LANNING.

Exclusive distributors:
Music Sales Limited
Newmarket Road, Bury St Edmunds, Suffolk IP33 3YB.
This book © Copyright 2002 Chester Music

Music setting by Jerry Lanning.
Printed in the United Kingdom.

Chester Music

CONTENTS

JOLLY OLD ST NICHOLAS

Words & Music by Vaughn Horton

Play all the quavers full length (not *staccato*) and articulate them clearly.

GOOD KING WENCESLAS

Traditional

Make all the notes full length, with a strong sound but clearly articulated.

AWAY IN A MANGER

Words traditional, music by W. J. Kirkpatrick

Try to think in four-bar phrases, not two.

WE THREE KINGS OF ORIENT ARE

Words & music by J. H. Hopkins

Make the tempo fast enough for you to feel one in a bar rather than three.
At the same time your playing should be smooth and relaxed.

SILENT NIGHT

Words by Joseph Mohr, music by Franz Grüber

A very smooth and sustained sound is needed for this well-known carol.

THE BIRDS

Czech traditional

Try to give the 'cuckoo calls' in this plaintive little carol a different sound and articulation.

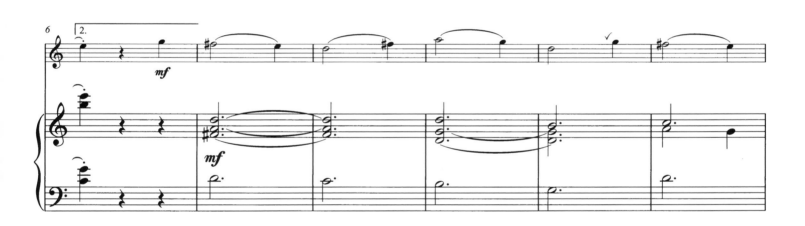

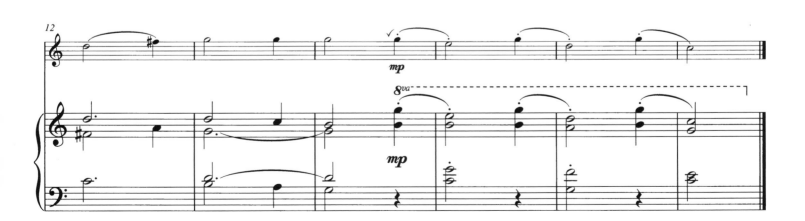

I SAW MOMMY KISSING SANTA CLAUS

Words & Music by Tommie Connor

Try for a very smooth and even sound. Keep the dotted rhythms relaxed.

WHEN SANTA GOT STUCK
UP THE CHIMNEY

Words & Music by Jimmy Grafton

Make a gradual crescendo through bars 17 and 18 to the f in bar 19.

JINGLE BELL ROCK

Words & Music by Joseph Beal & James Boothe

This piece can be played exactly as written or else with a swing feel.
In the latter case you'll probably need to play it a little slower.

DING DONG! MERRILY ON HIGH

French traditional

From bar 9 keep the impetus going right through to the third beat of bar 14.

ROCKING

Czech traditional

Try to make bar 3 sound like an echo of bar 2.

ANGELS FROM THE REALMS OF GLORY

Words by J. Montgomery, music French traditional

This popular hymn tune needs to be played with a good deal of exuberance.

CHRISTMAS ALPHABET

Words & music by Buddy Kaye & Jules Loman

Keep a steady beat. The dotted rhythms should be quite relaxed.

I BELIEVE IN FATHER CHRISTMAS

Words & Music by Greg Lake & Peter Sinfield

Take care to play the rhythms really accurately in the main part of the song.
The piano part will give you plenty of support.

HAPPY XMAS (WAR IS OVER)

Words & Music by John Lennon & Yoko Ono

Be careful to count four dotted crotchet beats in every bar. Don't guess!

Moderately

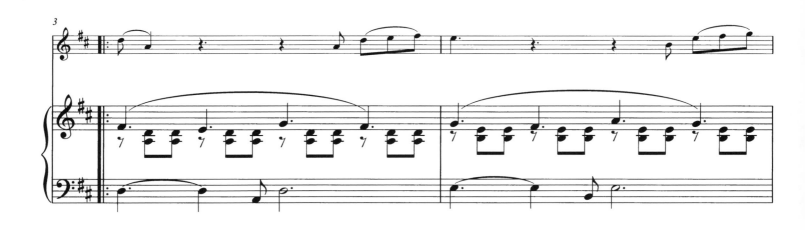

THE HOLLY AND THE IVY

Traditional

Make your playing neat and rhythmical.

DECK THE HALL

Welsh traditional

This one needs a good lively performance. Remember to repeat the first four bars.

THE FIRST NOWELL

Traditional

Don't let the tempo drag. Keep it moving forward, but without rushing.

O CHRISTMAS TREE

German traditional

Be careful to differentiate clearly between the rhythm of the
dotted quaver/semiquaver groups and the quaver pairs.

PATAPAN

French traditional

Adopt a steady march tempo for this carol. The accompaniment imitates the sound of drums.

LONELY THIS CHRISTMAS

Words & Music by Mike Chapman & Nicky Chinn

Smooth and even playing is needed here. Don't 'snatch' at any of the notes.